Blossom Creed

From one black girl to another.

SELF LOVE SOIL

SELF CARE WATER

Written by Rhashida Brown
Illustrated by Brittany James

To my earth Angel, my daughter Summer'Raine Brown
I give thanks for your light. Thank you for being my greatest
teacher. I pray that you always remember who you are and
stand in your power.

Love always,
Mommy

My melanin shines bright.
My brown skin glows.
I love the shape of my lips.
I love the shape of my nose.

I love the kinks, curls,
and coils in my hair.
I know they love it, too,
that's why they stare.

My confidence is high.
So high to the sky.

I love myself, and I love my brown sisters, too.
We are not each other's competition.
We don't believe in being rude.
We help our sisters fix their crown.
We don't like seeing each other down.

We acknowledge our
feelings first.
We are well aware of our
worth.

We understand the value of our mind.
We love to see our brown sisters shine.

Our physical health is important.
But our mental health is too.

Go, Blossom-Brown-Beauty, and be the best version of you.

Meet the Author
and the Artist

About the author

Rhashida Brown is a mother and a mental health professional and advocate. She is also the founder of Blossom Brown Beauty, a program and brand designed to empower young black and brown girls. Blossom Brown Beauty's mission is to extol pride in black and brown culture by helping young girls build healthy self-esteem, educate them on the importance of mental health and wellness, while influencing integrity and morale in their lives. It is Rhashida's hope that Blossom Brown Beauty's creed will positively impact young black and brown girls all over the world.

About the illustrator

Brittany (Britt) James, An artist in its truest form, Afromé founder Britt James' purpose is to capture the kaleidoscopic beauty of the Blackness. Inspired by her mental health struggles and deep love for her people, James created Afromé to serve the Black community with art that embodies the brilliance of and power in being melanated. It does just that. Afromé is a fantastical recreation of the Black world, breathing new life into familiar faces, hairstyles, skin, and bodies. James' work is genius for its simultaneous other worldliness and its portrayal of something so real and grounded in truth.Afromé is functional art that aims to serve the Black community in a multitude of ways. James' work is powerful and ever-evolving, bringing awareness to whitewashed history, fighting for injustice, and most importantly, providing healing and mental wellness to Black and Brown communities around the world.

To every girl reading this,
I hope you always proudly and loudly embrace
the words written in this book.
Always remember you matter.
You are uniquely and divinely made.
Your life matters.
Your mental health matters.
You are here for a reason.

BLOSSOM BROWN BEAUTY CREED

MY MELANIN SHINES BRIGHT.
MY BROWN SKIN GLOWS.
I LOVE THE SHAPE OF MY LIPS.
I LOVE THE SHAPE OF MY NOSE.
I LOVE THE KINKS, CURLS AND COILS IN MY HAIR.
I KNOW THEY LOVE IT TOO, THAT'S WHY THEY STARE.
MY CONFIDENCE IS HIGH.
SO HIGH TO THE SKY.
I LOVE MYSELF AND I LOVE MY BROWN SISTERS TOO.
WE ARE NOT EACH OTHER'S COMPETITION.
WE DON'T BELIEVE IN BEING RUDE.
WE HELP OUR SISTERS FIX THEIR CROWN.
WE DON'T LIKE SEEING EACH OTHER DOWN.
WE ACKNOWLEDGE OUR FEELINGS FIRST.
WE ARE WELL AWARE OF OUR WORTH.
WE UNDERSTAND THE VALUE OF OUR MIND.
WE LOVE TO SEE OUR BROWN SISTERS SHINE.
OUR PHYSICAL HEALTH'S IMPORTANT.
BUT OUR MENTAL HEALTH IS TOO.
GO BLOSSOM-BROWN-BEAUTY AND BE THE BEST
VERSION OF YOU.
CREATED BY:
RHASHIDA BROWN, FOUNDER

 BLOSSOMBROWNBEAUTY

Blossom Creed is not your average picture book. Blossom Creed is notable for its collection of positive affirmations, which extols pride in Black and Brown culture, while also highlighting the importance of mental health and wellness. This book is a must have and necessity on all household bookshelves for young girls.

CPSIA information can be obtained
at www.ICGtesting.com
Printed in the USA
LVHW071608160321
681670LV00025B/1498